This book belongs to

Date

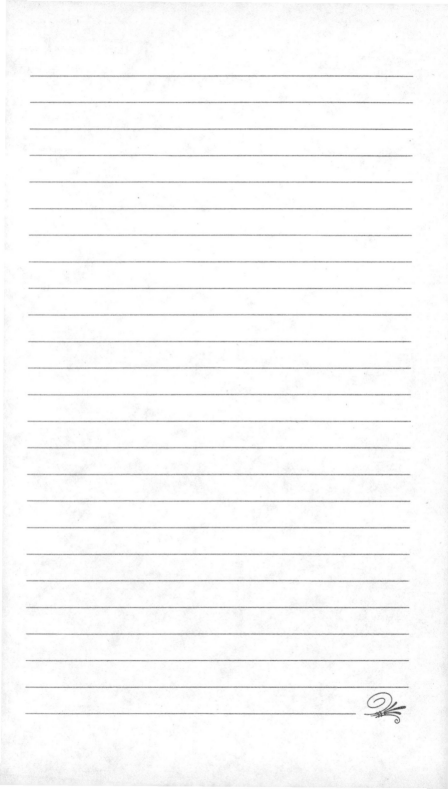

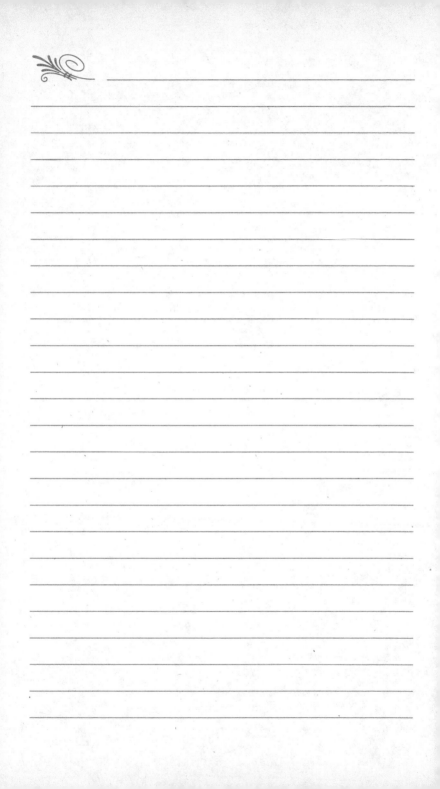

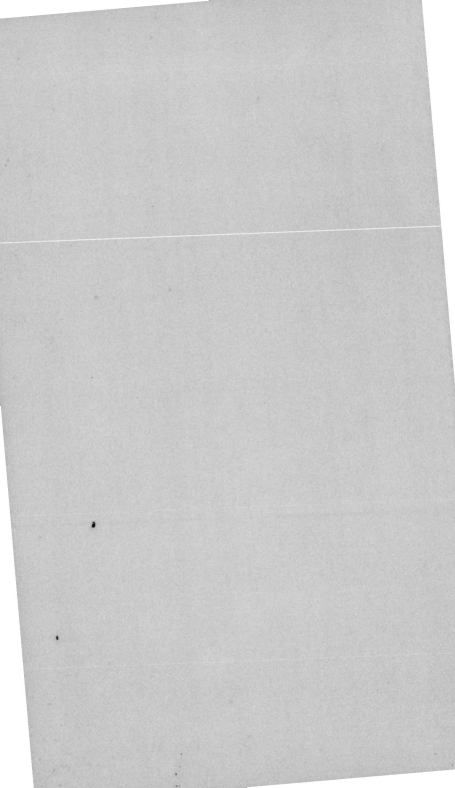